igloobooks

Published in 2021
First published in the UK by Igloo Books Ltd
An imprint of Igloo Books Ltd
Cottage Farm, NN6 0BJ, UK
Owned by Bonnier Books
Sveavägen 56, Stockholm, Sweden
www.igloobooks.com

1121 006
8 10 11 9 7
ISBN 978-1-78440-727-8

Written by Stephanie Moss
Illustrated by Caroline Pedler

Printed and manufactured in China

YOU AND ME
ALWAYS

igloobooks

You're my best friend in the world.
You're always by my side.

You're there as soon as I wake up
and stretch my arms out wide.

The times I love the most
are when we play out in the sun.

Even though we're very different,
we have lots of fun.

Though you might like to have a
walk or chase after your ball,
you play the games I want to
and don't seem to mind at all.

We see amazing things
when we both go out exploring.

Nobody could ever say
playtime with you is boring.

You're brave as brave can be and
you're strong and fearless, too.
I know I can do anything,
as long as I'm with you.

When I'm feeling poorly and
I can't go out to play...

... we snuggle up together
for a cosy duvet day.

Sometimes when I'm upset
or I feel like I'm on my own,
your big, wet, sloppy dog kisses
show me I'm not alone.

I tell you all my biggest secrets
and my worries, too.

There's no one else I'd trust to keep
them safe except for you.

At night-time when it's dark,
you're always there to comfort me.

You make me feel so safe,
there's nowhere else I'd rather be.

As I fall asleep,
I hold you close inside my heart.
I love you so very much,
I know we'll never be apart.

You're my best friend.

Always.